A Windy Day

Elspeth Graham

Illustrated by Ian Newsham

Oxford

"Look," said Josh.

"What is it?" said Kenny.

Kenny looked.

"What is it?" said Poppy.

Poppy looked.

"What is it?" said Jo.

Jo looked.

"What is it?" said Buzz.

Buzz looked.

"What is it?" said Mr Tucker.

CONTENTS

CHAPTER 1

NOT SO SIMPLE

It's time for a fun-filled day. You're about to enter a theme park! As you step through the gate, you see motion in all directions. Roller coasters zip down hills and through loops. The Ferris wheel goes round and round. As you take in all the sights and sounds, you might not notice the parts that make up these exciting rides. But if you look closely, you'll discover that much of the stomach-dropping fun at a theme park relies on simple machines.

Not sure you can spot them? Settle in and keep your eyes peeled. By the time the day is over, you'll be spotting simple machines wherever you go!

What are simple machines?

Theme parks are all about fun, right? Of course! But for us to have fun, machines have to do work. All simple machines make work easier for us.

A simple machine can work in different ways. It can change the direction or the magnitude of a force. A force is a push or a pull. The magnitude describes the size of the force. A simple machine can create big effects from small twists, turns or pulls. By changing the direction of a force, a simple machine can get something turning, twisting or spinning without much effort.

force push or pull

magnitude size of something

The Ferris wheel is one of the tallest rides at a theme park. It's also a simple machine!

5

What's the secret that makes simple machines do what they do? Simple machines use mechanical advantage. This means they reduce work. Work is what's done when a force moves something. Mechanical advantage allows you to use a little force to get a big pay-off.

There are six simple machines. These are pulleys, levers, wedges, inclined planes, wheels and axles, and screws. Each machine does a lot of work. And when simple machines work together, they can create non-stop fun at a theme park.

axle bar in the centre of a wheel around which a wheel turns

inclined plane sloped surface

lever bar that turns on a resting point and is used to lift items

mechanical advantage ability of a machine to reduce work

pulley grooved wheel turned by a rope, belt or chain

screw inclined plane wrapped around a pole that usually holds objects together

wedge device that moves to split things apart

SIMPLE MACHINES

pulley

lever

inclined plane

wedge

wheel and axle

screw

7

CHAPTER 2
PULL UP

Raise the flags

Before you even walk through the front gate of a theme park, you've already seen the work of a simple machine. Where? Look up. Can you see the row of flags waving over the park? Have you ever wondered how those flags got there? Do you think a worker went all the way up there to hang the flags? It's more likely that a pulley lifted them into place.

Pulley systems are attached to flagpoles. A pulley uses a grooved wheel looped with a cable to change the direction of a force. How does it do this? There is a wheel at the top of the flagpole. A cable wraps around it. As the worker pulls down on the cable, the flag goes up.

Six flags wave over the Six Flags Over Texas theme park in the United States.
The flags represent the different countries that have governed what is now Texas.

HUMAN-POWERED PARK

You can be a machine too! Take a trip to northern Italy. There you'll find the Ai Pioppi theme park. Except for just one ride, it is totally powered by humans and simple machines such as pulleys and levers. The park is filled with roller coasters, merry-go-rounds and other rides. But you won't find motors or electricity. People power all the rides with their legs and arms. Thankfully, the force of **gravity** acts on some rides to give visitors a rest and some hard-earned fun!

gravity force that pulls objects with mass together; gravity pulls objects down towards the centre of Earth

9

Pulleys on rides

Pulleys help with more than just raising flags. *Clack. Clack. Clack.* You know that noise! It's a roller coaster slowly climbing the first big hill. But guess what's pulling it up to that death-defying height? It's a pulley. The pulley that lifts a roller coaster is a chain wrapped around a gear. A motor turns the gear. The teeth in the gear grab the chain and pull it. This action lifts the ride in the same way a flag is raised.

The Zipper is one of the wildest rides at the theme park. Cars zip along on a spinning boom. A motor provides power to spin the wheels on each end of the boom. The cable pulls the cars around the wheels. What is the point of this pulley action? It causes one of the scariest parts of the ride – the flipping of the cars as they speed around the ends of the boom.

boom long beam connected to a support

gear toothed wheel that fits into another toothed wheel; gears can change the direction of a force or can transfer power

A cable brings the cars around the boom of the Zipper ride.

BLOCK AND TACKLE

If one pulley is good, more than one is better. When two or more
pulleys are connected by a single cable, the mechanical advantage is
even greater. The mechanical device created by using more than one
pulley is called a block and tackle. Each additional pulley reduces the
force needed to lift something. Two pulleys require half the force.
Four pulleys require a quarter of the force.

CHAPTER 3

WHEEL AROUND

Wheel and axle

As you lurch to the top of the Ferris wheel, you can see for miles. But if you look down, you can see another simple machine at work. You're riding on it! The Ferris wheel is a simple machine called a wheel and axle.

In a wheel and axle, a large wheel is attached to a rod called an axle. The spin of the axle moves the large wheel. A little spin on the axle causes big movement of the wheel. The wheel and axle rotate at the same rate. But the larger wheel turns over a greater distance than the axle. On a Ferris wheel, a motor usually provides power to spin the axle.

Wheels and axles are everywhere at a theme park. The entertainer on a unicycle uses physical force on the axle to get the wheel turning. The brightly lit merry-go-round spins on an axle.

The Ferris wheel turns around a huge axle at its centre.

For a double-axle thrill check out the Scrambler. On this ride you'll spin in cars attached to a small wheel and axle. At the same time a larger wheel and axle in the centre of the ride spins.

FACT

Do you want to go on the fastest ride on the merry-go-round? The outside horses travel the fastest. Why? All the horses must travel around the circle in the same amount of time, but those on the outside have further to go. They have to travel faster.

More than one way to work

Wheels help reduce work in other ways too. Imagine trying to pull or push a bulky food stall without wheels across the theme park. Its bottom would scrape across the ground. This would create a force called friction. Friction is a resisting force caused when two objects rub together. It would make your stall hard to move.

A stall on wheels moves easily around the park. Only the wheels touch the ground. Wheels reduce friction. They make it much easier to move things. The bigger the wheels, the easier the stall will be to push. Larger wheels give you more pushing force and overcome friction better than small wheels.

Wheels and axles on carts and food stalls help workers move them around a park easily.

Now head over to the toilets. Grab the doorknob and turn it. There's no need to go any further! You've just used a wheel and axle. As you turned the knob, it created a force in the axle.

Inside a doorknob, an axle turns to release a latch.

This force opened the latch to open the door. In this case you supplied a force to the outside of the wheel, and it turned the axle. The force on the axle was much larger than you could have supplied by turning the axle without a knob. The bigger the doorknob, the greater the force you can supply to the axle when turning it.

friction force created when two objects rub together

CHAPTER 4

LIFT AND WEDGE

Up the inclined plane

Scramble up the ramp as you rush to find a seat on the Waltzers. You've probably never noticed the simple machine right under your feet! The ramp is called an inclined plane.

An inclined plane is a sloped surface. It has no moving parts. But that doesn't mean it can't help lessen the effort required to do something. It takes less force to move something up an inclined plane than lifting it straight up. With little effort you can race right up a ramp to get to the top of a platform. Imagine the work it would take to try to climb or jump up there without a ramp. The longer an inclined plane is, the less effort it takes to move up it. But of course you'll have to travel further to move higher!

You'll find inclined planes all over the park. Check out the big slides or the hills on the roller coaster track. Toss a ball up the inclined plane at the Skee-Ball game. The inclined plane allows you to gently throw the ball up and position it to hit your target. Workers use ramps to load or unload goods from lorries. The staircases you travel up are inclined planes too. They all help you to move up and down with little effort.

A ball zips up the inclined plane of a Skee-Ball game.

Down the inclined plane

Imagine dropping straight down from the top of the log flume ride. The landing would probably be really hard! Instead, the log travels along an inclined plane. It makes the landing gentler.

An inclined plane works against the force of gravity to help you safely move down from a high place. As you go down a slide, gravity tries to pull you straight down. But friction slows your movement down the inclined plane. Even the force from the inclined plane pushing back on you reduces the effect of gravity. You can move safely down the slide.

MORE INCLINED PLANES

An inclined plane doesn't have to be straight like a ramp. Have you ever driven up a mountain? The road twists around the mountain to move you very high with ease. The road is like a ramp, but it twists its way around instead of running straight up.

A log flume ride uses an inclined plane to help riders travel safely downwards.

FACT

The longest slide in the world is in London at the Queen Elizabeth Olympic Park. It stands 78 metres (256 feet) tall and is 178 metres (584 feet) long. Part of it is shaped like a corkscrew.

Wedges

Have you ever tried to ride side by side with a friend on the bumper cars? What happens if somebody tries pushing his or her car between yours? If a driver is able to create a small amount of separation between cars, he or she can probably wedge in and push your cars even further apart. This separation is caused by wedge action.

A wedge is a simple machine that causes separation by changing the direction of a force. Wedges are thicker on one end and tapered to a point on the other. An example is the axe the scary waxwork man is holding at the haunted house. Outside the theme park, an axe works to separate a chunk of wood into pieces. It changes a downward force into sideways pushing forces. That's its mechanical advantage.

When one bumper car pushes between two other cars, the middle car is acting like a wedge. Most wedges push things apart.

Are you ready for a cool drink or a tasty snack? The knife used to cut lemon slices for your lemonade is another wedge. Are you ready to get a slice of pizza? A worker at the food stall might have used a wedge called a pizza rocker to cut it.

CHAPTER 5

FLIP AND TWIST

Screws

Don't forget to head over to the entertainment tent to watch a show. But before you step into the tent, check out the anchors that hold it to the ground. These anchors are probably screws, another simple machine.

A screw is a simple machine with spiralled threads. Usually the threads wrap around a solid core. But some screws, such as corkscrews, are open spirals.

When a screw is twisted, its threads easily force their way into a solid object. A screw changes a twist into forward movement. Screws allow a small twist to become a big force. For the workers setting up a tent, twisting the anchors into the ground is much easier than pounding them in.

You'll see screws all over the theme park. Many metal parts of rides are held together with screws. Screws hold the parts of benches together. Screws also spiral into wood or metal to hang signs.

thread spiral part of a screw

Some tent cables are held by screws that twist into the ground.

Levers

You're up! Then you're down! And now you're hanging over the edge of a building more than 259 metres (850 feet) in the air! You are on the X-Scream on top of the Stratosphere in Las Vegas, USA. This hair-raising ride acts like a lever to change the ride's directions. A lever is a simple machine that uses a **beam** and a **fulcrum**. A beam is a long, straight rod. A fulcrum causes a beam to turn (pivot). A lever reduces the amount of effort needed to lift a load.

Have you ever been on a see-saw? Then you've seen a lever in action. You and a friend sit on the ends of the beam. The centre of the beam is connected to the fulcrum. As you push up, your friend is forced down.

beam long, heavy piece of wood, metal or other material used for support

fulcrum place where a lever pivots

The X-Scream hangs riders off the top of the Stratosphere in Las Vegas, USA.

THREE CLASSES OF LEVERS

There are three classes of levers. Each one has the load and fulcrum in a different location. In a class 1 lever the fulcrum is placed between the effort and load. In a class 2 lever the load is between the effort and the fulcrum. In a class 3 lever the effort is between the load and the fulcrum.

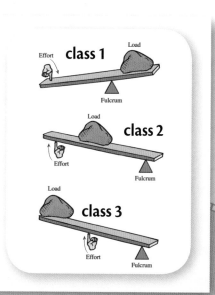

Not all levers look the same. The fulcrum is not always in the middle of the beam. Spoon some snow cone into your mouth. As you dig into this frozen treat, you are using a lever. When you take a scoop, your hand is the fulcrum. When you push down, the spoon lifts the treat out of the cone. The force you apply is magnified by the pivoting spoon.

Levers aren't just used as part of theme park rides. You'll see ride operators pushing or pulling levers to start and stop rides. Levers are often used for light switches. When you flip a switch, the fulcrum at its base turns the power on or off. In some rides you get to control how high you go. You use a lever to control your height.

A spoon is a type of lever.

FACT

Many levers are used as tools. A crowbar is a lever that can easily pull out a nail.

CHAPTER 6

ADD THEM UP

There's no doubt that simple machines increase the fun at a theme park. But simple machines don't always do the work alone. More than one simple machine can work together. When simple machines work together, they make a **complex machine**. Many rides and attractions use wheels and axles, pulleys and levers together. Hop on a roller coaster. It uses pulleys and inclined planes for heart-pounding fun.

Wherever you go at a theme park, you'll see machines. Whether simple or complex, machines work for you. Now you know where to find them at a theme park. Where else can you find these machines working for you?

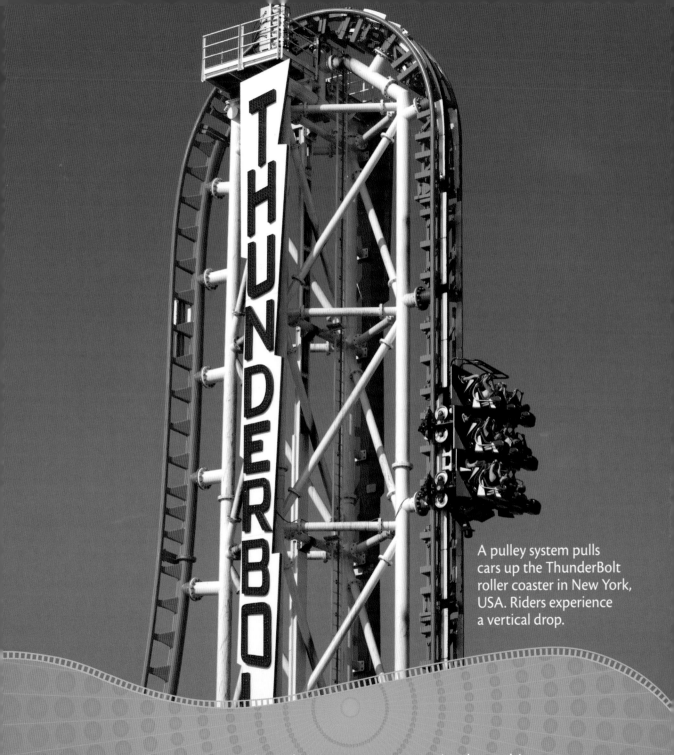

A pulley system pulls cars up the ThunderBolt roller coaster in New York, USA. Riders experience a vertical drop.

complex machine machine that uses two or more simple machines

GLOSSARY

axle bar in the centre of a wheel around which a wheel turns

beam long, heavy piece of wood, metal or other material used for support

boom long beam connected to a support

complex machine machine that uses two or more simple machines

force push or pull

friction force created when two objects rub together

fulcrum place where a lever pivots

gear toothed wheel that fits into another toothed wheel; gears can change the direction of a force or can transfer power

gravity force that pulls objects with mass together; gravity pulls objects down towards the centre of Earth

inclined plane sloped surface

lever bar that turns on a resting point and is used to lift items

magnitude size of something

mechanical advantage ability of a machine to reduce work

pulley grooved wheel turned by a rope, belt or chain

screw inclined plane wrapped around a pole that usually holds objects together

thread spiral part of a screw

wedge device that moves to split things apart

COMPREHENSION QUESTIONS

1. Waltzer cars spin on a wavy platform as they rotate in a circle. What simple machines are at work on this ride?

2. Name two simple machines that could help you get to the top of a skyscraper.

3. What do you think would happen if you moved the fulcrum of a lever? Use reference books or the internet to find information to support your answer.

FIND OUT MORE

BOOKS

How Machines Work, David Macaulay (DK Children, 2015)

Making Machines with Levers (Simple Machine Projects), Chris Oxlade (Raintree, 2016)

Making Machines with Pulleys (Simple Machine Projects), Chris Oxlade (Raintree, 2016)

WEBSITE

www.dkfindout.com/uk/science/simple-machines
Find out more about simple machines.

INDEX

Theme Park Science

SIMPLE MACHINES

at the
THEME PARK

by Tammy Enz

Raintree is an imprint of Capstone Global Library Limited, a company incorporated in England and Wales having its registered office at 264 Banbury Road, Oxford, OX2 7DY – Registered company number: 6695582

www.raintree.co.uk
myorders@raintree.co.uk

Edited by Carrie Braulick Sheely
Designed by Tracy McCabe
Original illustrations © Capstone Global Library Limited 2020
Picture research by Eric Gohl
Production by Kathy McColley
Originated by Capstone Global Library Ltd
Printed and bound in India

978 1 4747 8514 3 (hardback)
978 1 4747 8518 1 (paperback)

British Library Cataloguing in Publication Data
A full catalogue record for this book is available from the British Library.

Acknowledgements
We would like to thank the following for permission to reproduce photographs: Alamy: Isaac74, 9 (bottom), Q-Images, 9 (top), Richard Green, 17; Capstone: 7; Getty Images: Dorling Kindersley, 15; iStockphoto: Aneese, 29, onfilm, 21, PIMpoon9, 27; Newscom: John Greim Photography, 19; Shutterstock: Colin Dewar, back cover (background), 1 (background), 11, corbac40, 25 (bottom), Dana Ward, 25 (top), footageclips, 5, Gyvafoto, 20, Hintau Aliaksei, 22, Krylovochka, cover (bottom), 1 (bottom), Rudmer Zwerver, 23, Sanga Park, cover (top), 13, Sergey Edentod, 14. Design elements: Shutterstock.